# TV SONGS OF THE 90's

## FIRST EDITION

Copyright © 1991 CPP/Belwin, Inc.
15800 N.W. 48th Avenue, Miami, Florida 33014

Editor: Carol Cuellar

# CONTENTS

# I WISH I KNEW

## (Theme From "The Trials of Rosie O'Neill")

Words and Music by
CAROLE KING

I Wish I Knew - 3 - 1

6

*Theme from*

# TWIN PEAKS

Music by
ANGELO BADALAMENTI

Twin Peaks - 3 - 1

Some - times you wan - na go___ where ev - 'ry-bod - y knows___ your name,___ and they're al - ways glad___ you came.___ You wan - na be___ where you can see___ our trou - bles are all the same.___ You wan - na be___ where ev - 'ry-bod-y knows

# MERCY MERCY ME
## (The Ecology)

Words and Music by
MARVIN GAYE

Mercy Mercy Me - 2 - 1

1. Ah things ain't what they used to be, no, no
   Oil wasted on the ocean and upon
   Our seas fish full of mercury, Ah.

2. Ah things ain't what they used to be
   What about this over crowded land
   How much more abuse from man can she stand?

# THEME FROM FERRIS BUELLER

## (From the Television Series "FERRIS BUELLER")

Music by
GLENN JORDAN

Theme From Ferris Bueller - 2 - 1

# IF THIS ISN'T LOVE
### (From the Television Show "AS THE WORLD TURNS")

Words and Music by
GLORIA SKLEROV and STEVE DORFF

If This Isn't Love - 4 - 1

If This Isn't Love - 4 - 2

If This Isn't Love - 4 - 3

# "AMERICAN DREAMER" THEME

(From the T.V. Series "AMERICAN DREAMER")

Words and Music by
PETER LEINHEISER

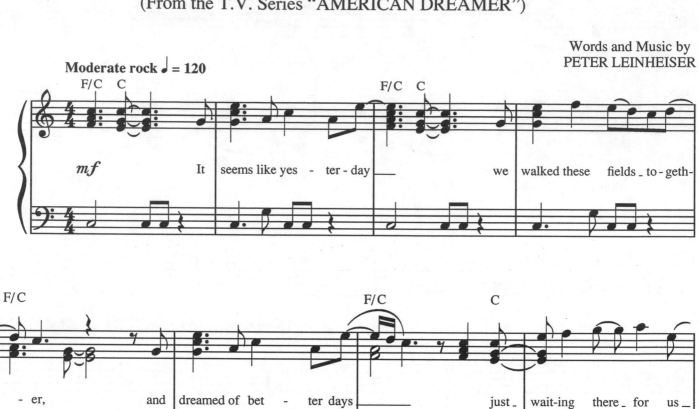

"American Dreamer" Theme - 2 - 1

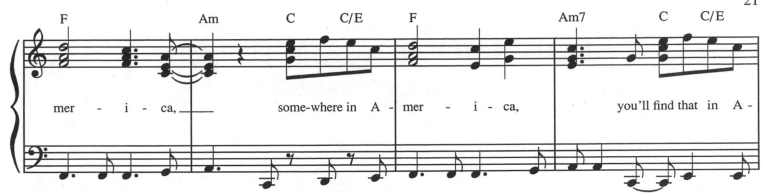

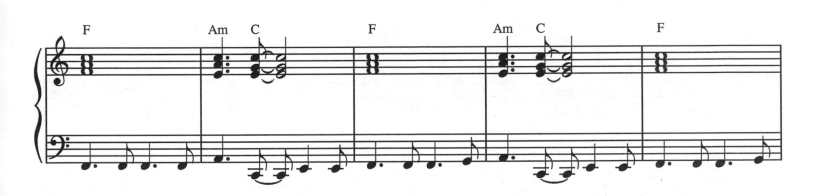

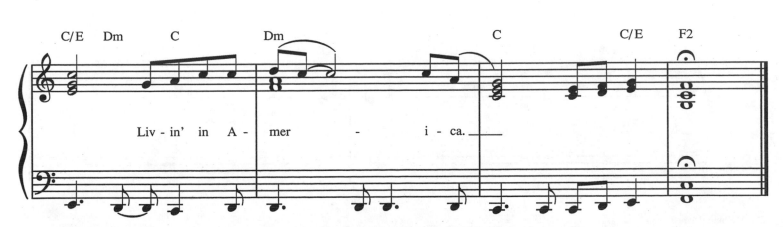

"American Dreamer" Theme - 2 - 2

# DOWN HOME (MAIN TITLE)

### (From the TV Series "DOWN HOME")

By STEWART LEVIN

Down Home (Main Title) - 2 - 1

# E.A.R.T.H. FORCE (MAIN TITLE)
### (From the Television Series "E.A.R.T.H. FORCE")

Rock ♩ = 112

Music by CORY LERIOS and
JOHN D'ANDREA

# THEME FROM "SONS AND DAUGHTERS"

(From the Television Series "SONS AND DAUGHTERS")

Music by
STEVE DORFF

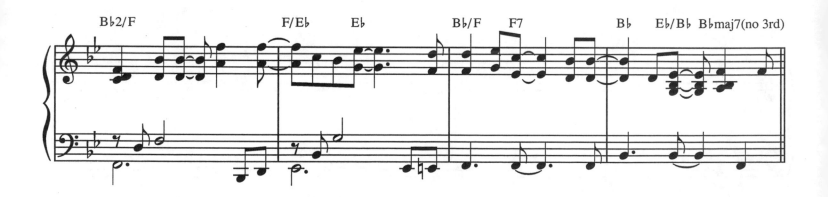

Theme from "Sons and Daughters" - 2 - 1

Theme from "Sons and Daughters" - 2 - 2

# I HEARD IT THROUGH THE GRAPEVINE

Words and Music by
NORMAN WHITFIELD and
BARRETT STRONG

Oo_____ Bet you're won-d'ring how I knew 'bout your_ plans_

— to make me blue with some oth - er guy_____ that you knew be - fore

I Heard It Through The Grapevine - 4 - 1

I Heard It Through The Grapevine - 4 - 3

I Heard It Through The Grapevine - 4 - 4

# ALL MY ROWDY FRIENDS
# ARE COMING OVER TONIGHT

By HANK WILLIAMS, JR.

Rock 'n Roll ♩ = 144

All My Rowdy Friends - 5 - 1

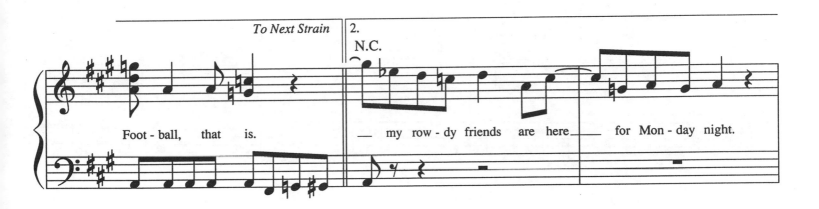

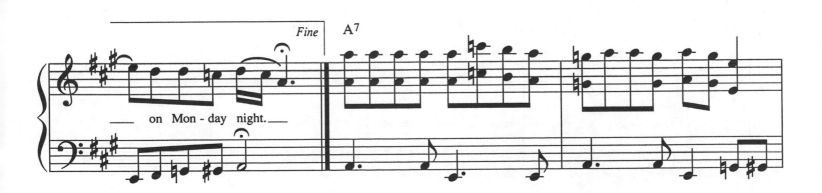

When those___

A⁷

red-hot teams___ play un-der the lights,___ those X-s and Os___ just seem___ to ig-nite.___ Now I

*D.S. 𝄋 al Fine*

know some guys___ that are read-y to blitz___ and some big old dudes___will be tak-ing their licks.___ I'll bet they're

# TIM CONWAY'S FUNNY AMERICA (MAIN TITLE)
## (From the TV Series "TIM CONWAY'S FUNNY AMERICA")

Music by TOM CHASE and
STEVE RUCKER

# ANOTHER WORLD
## (Theme)

By
JOHN LEFFLER and
RALPH SCHUCKETT

Another World - 3 - 1

Another World - 3 - 2

*Verse 2:*
All my life I've been called a hopeless romantic,
Waiting for my prince to take me away.
But when I found you I felt different,
Than I've ever felt before.
Suddenly I was taking no chances
By walking through your door.
You are my . . .
*(To Chorus:)*

# BRAND NEW LIFE

Words by
**BLAKE HUNTER** and
**MARTY COHAN**

Music by
**LARRY CARLTON** and
**ROBERT KRAFT**

Brand New Life - 3 - 1

Nights are long __ but you might a-wak-en. A brand new life, __ brand new life, brand new life a - round __ the bend. ____

# CHANGING KEYS
### (Wheel of Fortune Theme)

Music by
MERV GRIFFIN

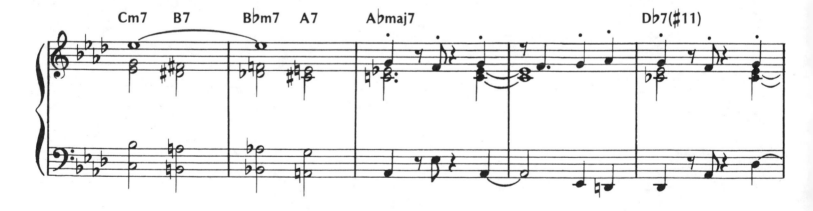

Changing Keys - 4 - 1

# DEAR JOHN

Words and Music by
JOHN SULLIVAN

Dear John - 2 - 1

# FRIDAY THE 13TH - THE SERIES

By
FRED MOLLIN

Friday The 13th - The Series - 2 - 1

Friday The 13th - The Series - 2 - 2

*From the Television Series "It's Garry Shandling's Show"*

# GARRY'S CLOSING THEME

By JOEY CARBONE

Garry's Closing Theme - 2 - 1

Garry's Closing Theme - 2 - 2

# GEORGIA ON MY MIND

Lyric by STUART GORRELL

Music by HOAGY CARMICHAEL

Georgia On My Mind - 4 - 1

Melodies bring memories
That linger in my heart.
Make me think of Georgia,
Why did we ever part?
Some sweet day when blossoms fall
And all the world's a song,
I'll go back to Georgia,
'Cause that's where I belong.

# HALL OR NOTHING
## (THEME FROM THE ARSENIO HALL SHOW)

By
ARSENIO HALL

**Moderate rock** ♩ = 120

*(Bass may be played 8va)*

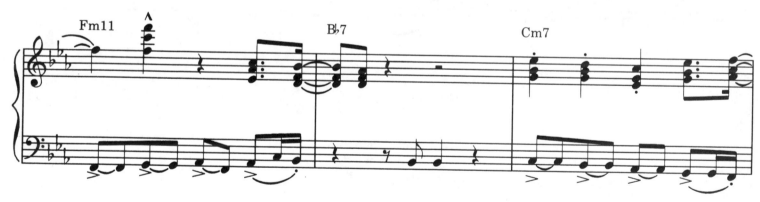

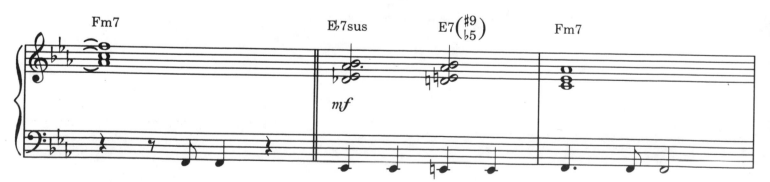

Hall Or Nothing - 2 - 1

# WINGS (MAIN TITLE)
## (Sonata in A)

By
FRANZ SCHUBERT

Music Adapted and Arranged by
ANTONY COOKE

Moderately ♩ = 116

*From the Television Series "It's Garry Shandling's Show"*

# IT'S GARRY'S THEME

Lyrics by
**GARRY SHANDLING**
**and ALAN ZWEIBEL**

Music by
**JOEY CARBONE**

It's Garry's Theme - 2 - 1

Verse 2:
This is the theme to Garry's show;
The opening theme to Garry's show.
This is the music that you hear
As you watch the credits.
We're almost to the part
Of where I start to whistle,
Then we'll watch "It's Garry Shandling's Show."

*Theme From The Paramount Televsion Series "MACGYVER"*

# MACGYVER

By RANDY EDELMAN

Macgyver - 2 - 1

Macgyver - 2 - 2

# THE MASTERPIECE
### (Theme from The Masterpiece Theatre)

By
J.J. MOURET and
PAUL PARNES

The Masterpiece - 3 - 1

The Masterpiece - 3 - 2

The Masterpiece - 3 - 3

*From Paramount Television and Video Distribution*

# ENTERTAINMENT TONIGHT

Music by
MICHAEL MARK

# STAR TREK®
# THE NEXT GENERATION
(Main Title)

By
ALEXANDER COURAGE, GENE RODDENBERRY
and JERRY GOLDSMITH

Star Trek The Next Generation - 4 - 1

# THEME FROM ALF

Music by
TOM KRAMER and
ALF CLAUSEN

Theme From Alf - 2 - 1

Theme From Alf - 2 - 2

*From the Television Series "THE GOLDEN GIRLS"*

# THANK YOU FOR BEING A FRIEND

Words and Music by
ANDREW GOLD

# THEME FROM GUIDING LIGHT

Words and Music by
ROB MOUNSEY

Theme From Guiding Light - 2 - 1

# THEME FROM
# "THE JOAN RIVERS SHOW"

Music by
MIKE POST

Joan Rivers - 2 - 1

# THEME FROM STAR SEARCH

Composed by
JOEY CARBONE

Theme From Star Search - 2 - 1

Theme From Star Search - 2 - 2

*Theme from the Embassy Television Series "227"*

# THERE'S NO PLACE LIKE HOME

Words and Music by
RAY COLCORD

There's No Place Like Home - 2 - 1

There's No Place Like Home - 2 - 2

# WAR OF THE WORLDS' SECOND WAVE

## Opening Credits Theme

Words and Music by
STEVEN COHEN and FRED MOLLIN

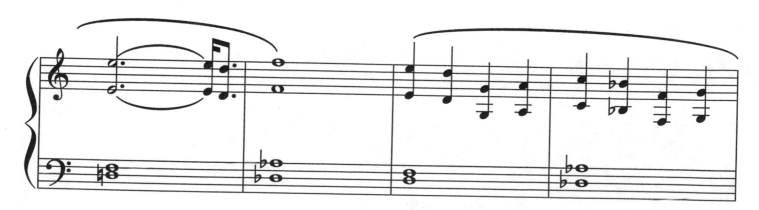

*War of the Worlds' Second Wave - 2 -1*

# JEOPARDY THEME

Music by
MERV GRIFFIN

Moderately bright ♩ = 132

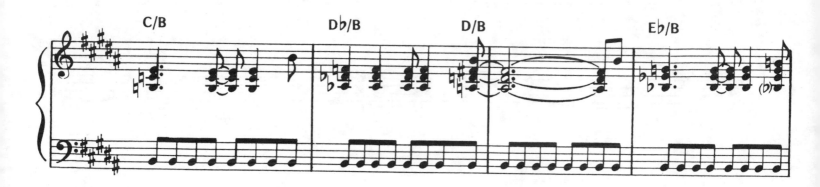

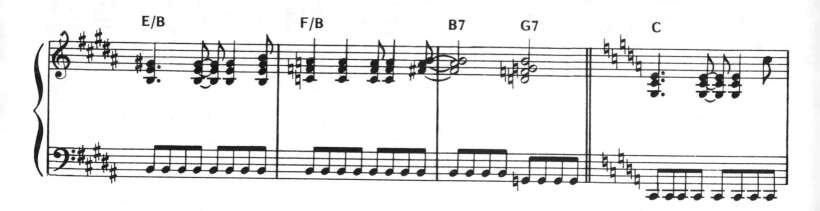

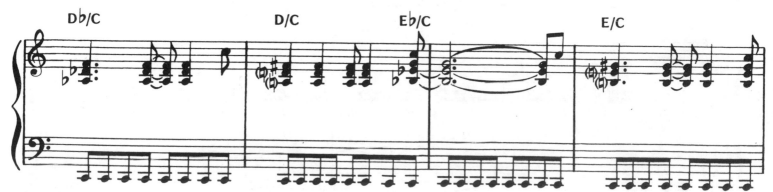

Jeopardy Theme - 3 - 1

Jeopardy Theme - 3 - 2

MAIN THEME *from the PARAMOUNT Television Series*

# WAR OF THE WORLDS

Music by
BILLY THORPE and
LAWRENCE H. BROWN

**Heavy march beat**

War Of The Worlds - 3 - 1

War Of The Worlds - 3 - 3

# THE WORLD TURNS ON AND ON

Words and Music by
JACK CORTNER

The World Turns On and On - 2 - 1

# WE ARE ONE

Words and Music by
MARIJOHN WILKIN